Multiplying and Dividing

Ruth Merttens

B.A., M.Ed.

Illustrated by Colin Mier

5 ... 10 ... 15 ... 20 ...

Count the bees by making groups of **5**s. The 1st one is done for you.

How many groups of **5** are there?

Can you skip count by **5s**? Fill in the boxes.

| 5 | ▶ | 10 | ▶ | | ▶ | 20 | ▶ | | ▶ | | ▶ | 35 |

Now can you go on?

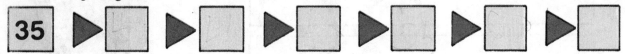

| 35 | ▶ | | ▶ | | ▶ | | ▶ | | ▶ | | ▶ | |

Skip counting by **10s** is even easier. Fill in the boxes.

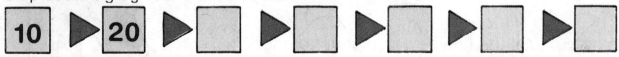

| 10 | ▶ | 20 | ▶ | | ▶ | | ▶ | | ▶ | | ▶ | |

Now skip count by **10s**, starting with **4**.
Fill in the boxes using a number line, a calculator
or your fingers to help you.

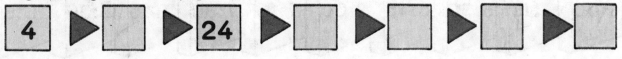

| 4 | ▶ | | ▶ | 24 | ▶ | | ▶ | | ▶ | | ▶ | |

3

Holiday plans

Prop and Prep are going on vacation.

1. How long does it take to fly from London to Paris?

2. How long does the plane stop in Paris?

3. How long does it take to fly from Paris to Rome?

4. How long does the plane stop in Rome?

5. Between which two cities is the longest flight?

Write your answers here.

1.

2.

3.

4.

5.

You can use the line below to count along.
Each suitcase you move along is **15** minutes.

6:00 6:15 6:30 6:45 7:00 7:15 7:30 7:45 8:00 8:15

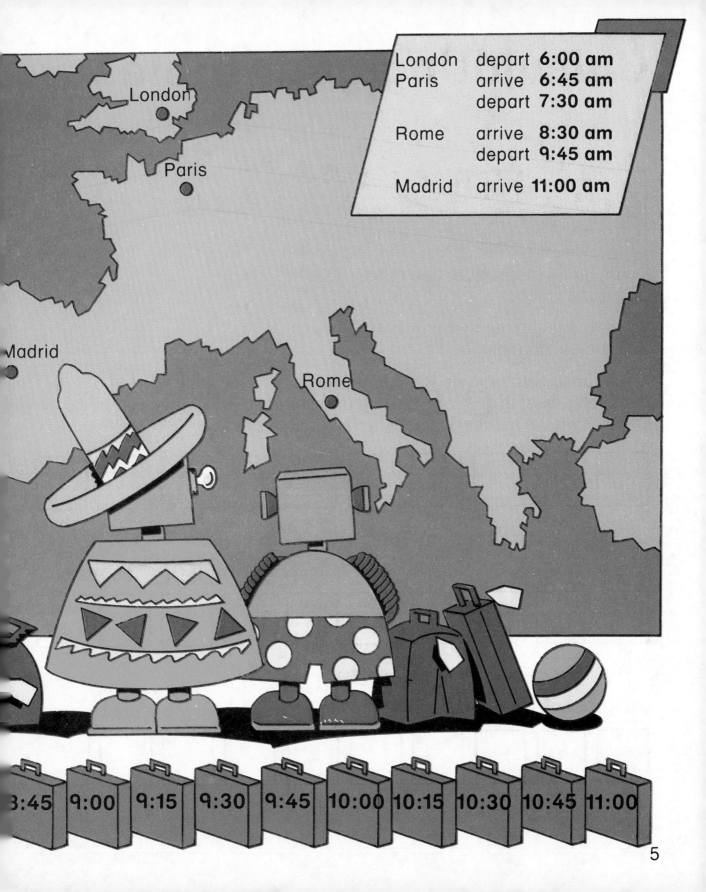

London	depart	**6:00 am**
Paris	arrive	**6:45 am**
	depart	**7:30 am**
Rome	arrive	**8:30 am**
	depart	**9:45 am**
Madrid	arrive	**11:00 am**

London

Paris

Madrid

Rome

8:45 | 9:00 | 9:15 | 9:30 | 9:45 | 10:00 | 10:15 | 10:30 | 10:45 | 11:00

5

Calculating your tables

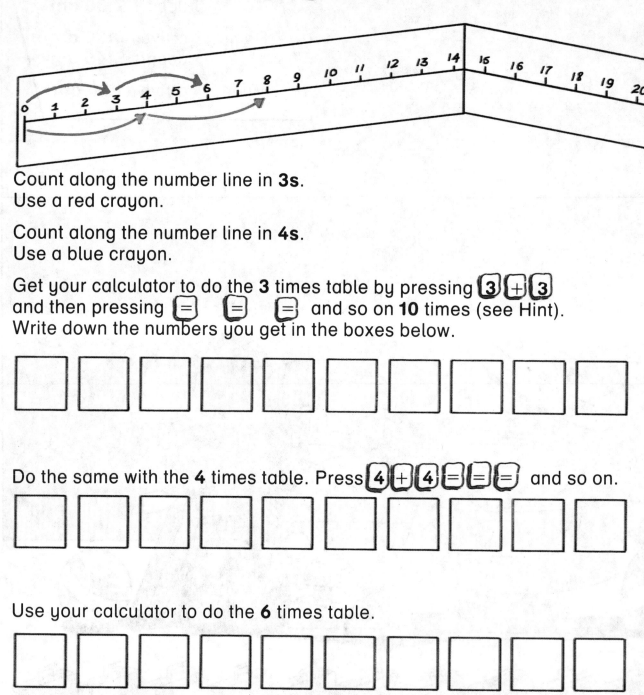

Count along the number line in **3s**.
Use a red crayon.

Count along the number line in **4s**.
Use a blue crayon.

Get your calculator to do the **3** times table by pressing ③ ⊕ ③
and then pressing ⊜ ⊜ ⊜ and so on **10** times (see Hint).
Write down the numbers you get in the boxes below.

Do the same with the **4** times table. Press ④ ⊕ ④ ⊜ ⊜ ⊜ and so on.

Use your calculator to do the **6** times table.

Note to Parents

Children are using a calculator here to learn their tables by adding. This reinforces the concept of multiplication as repeated addition.

Hint

With some calculators you may need to press **3 + +** then **=** repeatedly.
Many calculators are different.
You may have to experiment a little!

Do you notice anything about the numbers in the **3** times table and those in the **6** times table?

Shopping list

You have **$5.00** to spend.
Can you choose what you want
to buy from this list?

Dominoes	$2.60
Pencil	20¢
Toy car	$2.50
Robot	$2.50
Toy pony	$3.50
Crayons	80¢
Stickers	60¢
Rubber stamp	20¢
Comic book	40¢
Scissors	$2.40
Glue	40¢
Felt-tips	$2.20
Coloring book	$1.00

Use your calculator to try out ideas until you have a
list of things you can afford with your **$5.00**.

You can check to see if you can afford all the things
you have chosen by coloring in the spaces below.
(See the example on the top of page 9 to help you.)

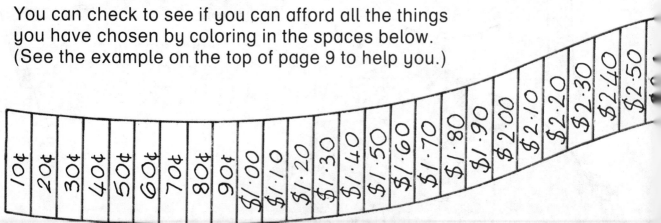

Add up the prices on your list one at a time to see if they all fit. Try it out in pencil first!

Write your list here.

10¢ 20¢ 30¢ 40¢ 50¢ 60¢

20¢   40¢

$2.90 $3.00 $3.10 $3.20 $3.30 $3.40 $3.50 $3.60 $3.70 $3.80 $3.90 $4.00 $4.10 $4.20 $4.30 $4.40 $4.50 $4.60 $4.70 $4.80 $4.90 $5.00

Grab and group

You will need about **40-50** small objects such as counters, blocks or dried beans or peas! It is best to play this game with someone else. See who can score the highest total in **6** turns.

Take turns scooping up one large handful of counters or beans.

Group them in **2s**. If they group exactly, give yourself **2** points.

Group them in **3s**. If they group exactly, give yourself **3** points.

Group them in **4s**. If they group exactly, give yourself **4** points.

Group them in **5s**. If they group exactly, give yourself **5** points.

Group them in **6s**. If they group exactly, give yourself **6** points.

Fill in this chart as you play.
Write your numbers in the correct spaces below.

Points	2	3	4	5	6	Total	Number scooped
My turn							
Your turn							
My turn							
Your turn							
My turn							
Your turn							

Nice numbers group in **2s** and **3s**.
Write nice numbers in here.

Some numbers are a little "nasty."
They won't group at all.
Write nasty numbers in here.

Drawing numbers

If we try drawing numbers in rows (of the same length), **nice** numbers (the ones that you found would group exactly on pages 10 and 11) can be drawn in many ways. **Nasty** numbers can only be drawn in one way. **20** is drawn here for you in **3** ways.

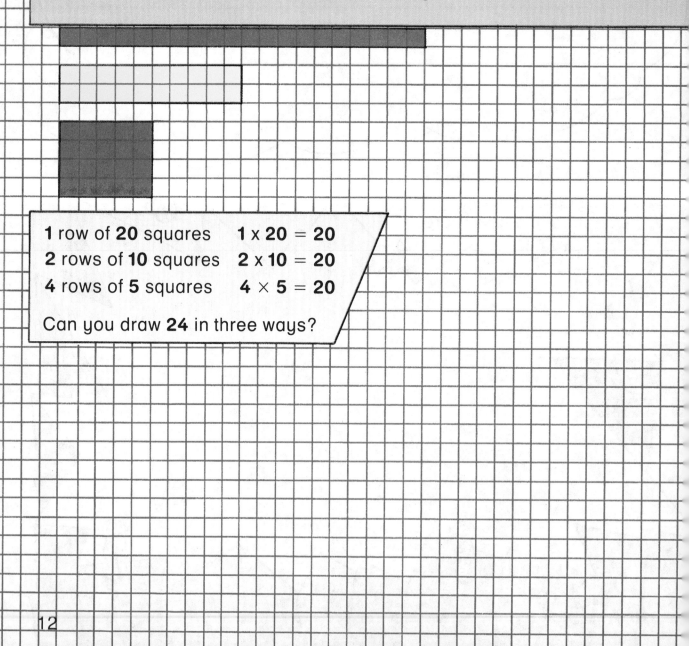

1 row of **20** squares   **1** x **20** = **20**

2 rows of **10** squares   **2** x **10** = **20**

4 rows of **5** squares   **4** × **5** = **20**

Can you draw **24** in three ways?

Ten times over

Start with number **5**. Color it red on the square.
Add on **10**. Color your answer red on the square.
Add on **10** more. Color your answer red.
Keep on going until you run out of squares.

What do you notice about the numbers you have colored red?

Start with **7**. Color it blue on the square.
Add on **10**. Color your answer blue on the square.
Keep on going until you run out of squares.

0	1	2	3	4	5	6	7	8	9
10	11	12	13	14	15	16	17	18	19
20	21	22	23	24	25	26	27	28	29
30	31	32	33	34	35	36	37	38	39
40	41	42	43	44	45	46	47	48	49
50	51	52	53	54	55	56	57	58	59
60	61	62	63	64	65	66	67	68	69
70	71	72	73	74	75	76	77	78	79
80	81	82	83	84	85	86	87	88	89
90	91	92	93	94	95	96	97	98	99

What happens if you start with **3**?

Write the numbers in these boxes.
Don't actually color them on the square.

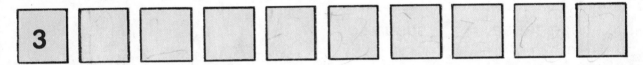

Count the boxes you filled in. _____

How many times did you add **10**? _____

What number do you get if you add another **10**? _____

What are **10** groups of **10**? _____

This explains why you started with **3** and ended with _____

Rep-Tiles

This big shape can be divided into **4** little shapes which are all the same shape as the big shape.

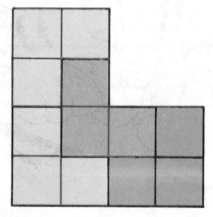

Remember, the area is the number of squares that a shape covers.

How many squares does the big shape cover?

Big shape's area = _____ squares.

How many squares does each little shape cover?

Little shape's area = _____ squares.

Is each little shape the same? | Yes/No |

Can you draw an even bigger similar shape which has **2** sides of **8** squares long? Use the space on the next page. One side is drawn for you.

How many little shapes can fit inside the big shape you have drawn?_____

What is your shape's area?_____ squares.

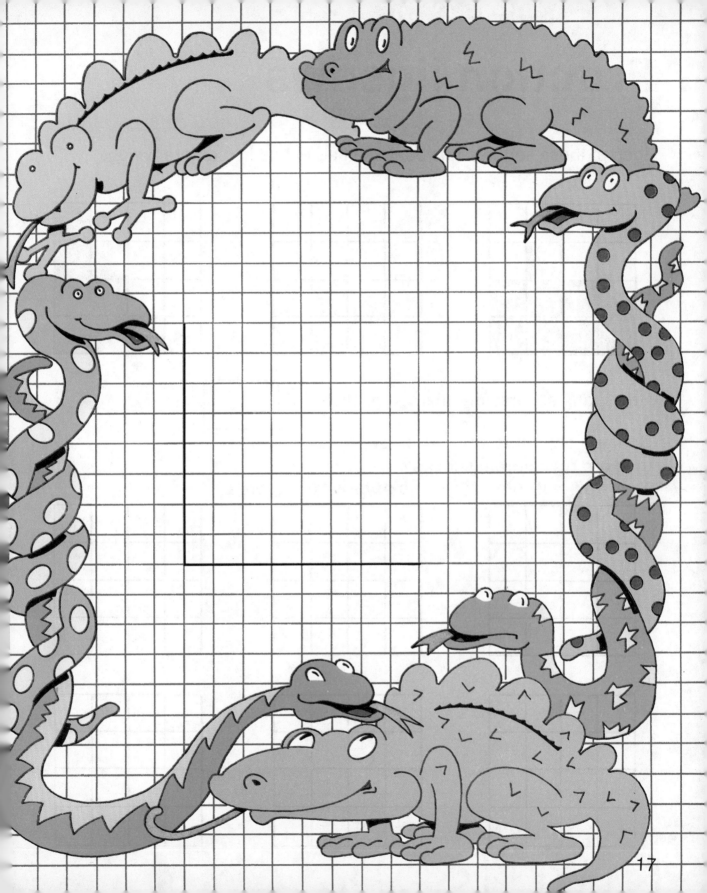

Fraction jigsaws

Each of these squares has been divided in half in a different way.

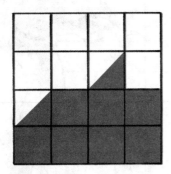 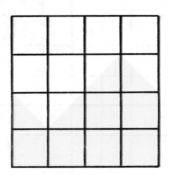 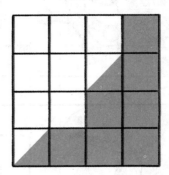

How many squares are there in each half?

Can you divide the squares below in half so that
they are **all** different shapes?
Each half must have the same **number** of squares.

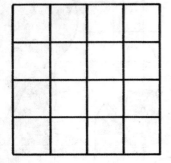 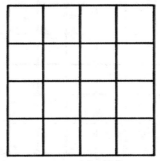 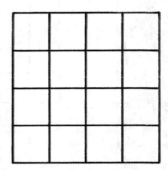

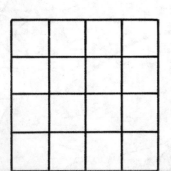 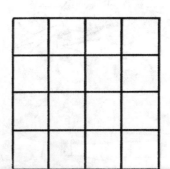 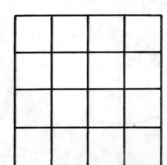

Can you divide the squares below into **thirds**?
The thirds should all be the same size (each have the same **area**),
but be different **shapes**.

How many squares are there
in each third?

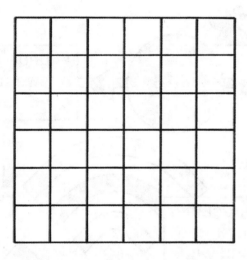

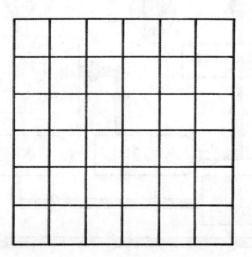

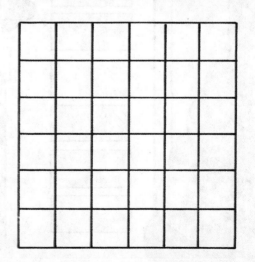

Divide and rule...

Start at the beginning. Follow the arrows. When you reach the end, write down your answer in one of the boxes.

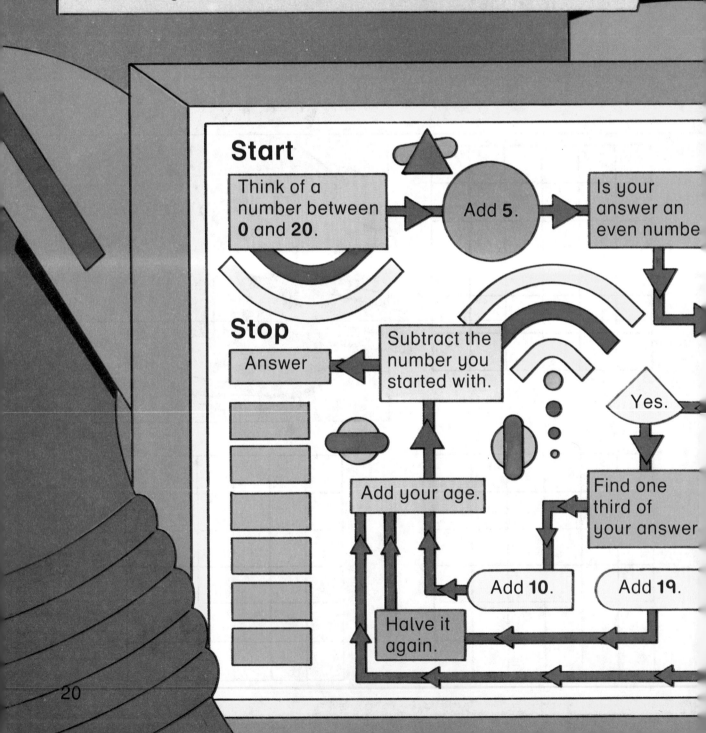

Start

Think of a number between **0** and **20**.

Add **5**.

Is your answer an even numbe

Stop

Answer

Subtract the number you started with.

Yes.

Add your age.

Find one third of your answer

Add **10**.

Add **19**.

Halve it again.

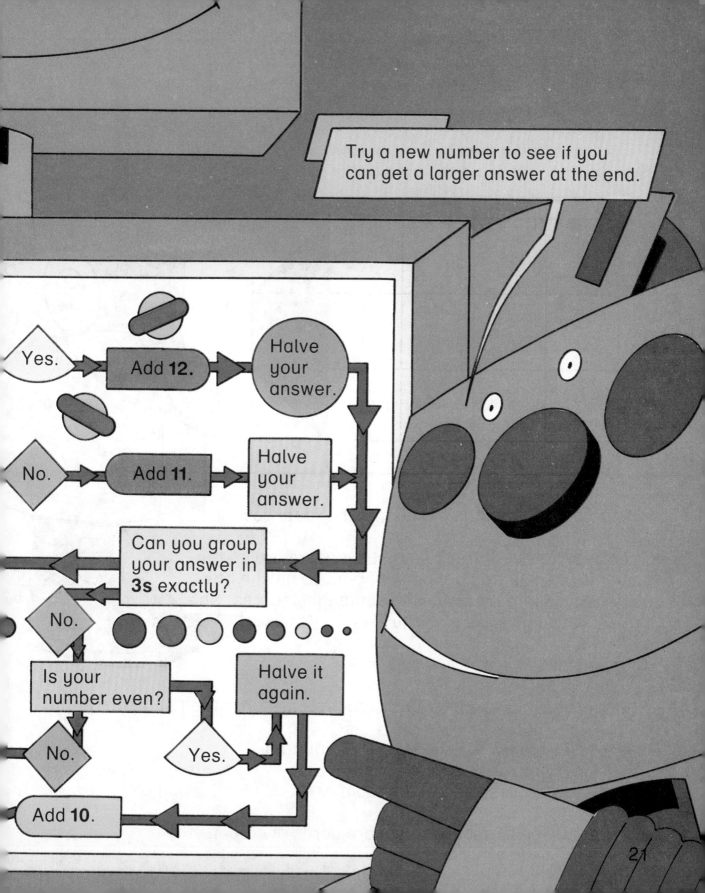

Areas of rooms

Prep has drawn a plan of her bedroom.
She wants to measure the area of her room to buy some carpet for it.

The area is the number of squares the room covers.

Prep has drawn her room so that every square on the paper is one square yard on the floor. So all she has to do to measure the area is to count the squares. She says there are **3** rows of **4** squares.

3 groups of 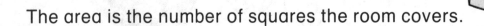 = **4** + **4** + **4** or **3** × **4** = ___

There is also a part on the end of the room, colored red on her plan.

It is ___ half squares + ___ square = ___squares.

Therefore, the total area of the room is **12** + **2** = ___ squares.

So Prep will need to buy___square yards of carpet.

Here is a plan of Prop's bedroom.

Count the numbers of squares in rows.
There are_____rows of **4** squares.

4 groups of **4**

The part on the end colored red is_____whole squares and_____halves.

The total area   squares.

Can you draw in some furniture for Prep and Prop? Try to make it the right size to fit their rooms.

To Parents

The math workbooks in **The Parent and Child Program** are an extension of the activity books. The exercises and games in this workbook reinforce and practice skills introduced in the activity book, **Multiplying Fun**.

Enjoy it! Children enjoy doing things with a parent. However, if an activity is proving too difficult, or the child becomes tired, leave it until another time. This book contains a variety of activities and inevitably each child will find some more stimulating than others.

Practical skill application: The approach to mathematics in **The Parent and Child Program** reflects the important role played by practical application of skills in children's learning. There is now a strong emphasis in math teaching on "hands-on" learning experiences. Through working with real objects, children come to **their own understanding of mathematical concepts**. To meet this goal, the math books throughout the Program contain numerous practical activities you can do at home.

Relating math to real life: mathematics plays an important part in all our lives. Children can benefit a great deal from relating their learning of math at school to things they do at home. The books in this series aim to help parents make those links; many of the topics covered can be extended into everyday activities such as shopping, cooking, traveling and so on.

Multiplying and dividing: in this book children are working with big numbers, using the methods of addition and subtraction they have learned earlier. By grouping things in equivalent sets, we introduce the concept of multiplication. Visual images, such as the number line, are provided to help children add and subtract. Practical activities, such as drawing a plan of a room to find its area, are included to help children explore specific concepts and see how what they are learning relates to their own everyday lives.

Calculators are introduced early in the Program to encourage exploration and discovery. They are used to reinforce mathematical concepts and practice procedures. They do not replace understanding. Calculator activities are provided after children learn number concepts and number facts, thereby enhancing understanding.

Your school and public library will have other books of interest, including:

Browne, Anthony. *Things I Like.*   NY: Random House, 1989.
Alexander, Sue. *Small Plays for Special Days.*   Boston: Houghton Mifflin, 1977.
Lionni, Leo. *The Biggest House in the World.*   NY: Knopf Dragonfly, 1989.